Hello, Everybody!

Illustrated by David Hill

ISBN 978-0-9855719-0-0
Printed in Mexico on FSC® paper
from well-managed forests

Music Together LLC
66 Witherspoon Street
Princeton NJ 08542
www.musictogether.com
(800) 728-2692

MUSIC TOGETHER®

Hello, Everybody!

Welcome!

Since 1987, Music Together has been bringing the Joy of Family Music® to young children and their families. This Singalong Storybook offers a new way to enjoy one of our best-loved Music Together songs. We invite you to sing it, read it, and use it as a starting point for conversation and imaginative play with your child.

Using the Book

If you're a Music Together family, you might start singing as soon as you turn the pages. But even if you've never attended one of our classes, you and your child can have hours of fun and learning with this Singalong Storybook. Read the story and enjoy the illustrations with your child, and then try some of the suggested activities that follow. The book can also help inspire artwork or enhance pre-literacy skills. You can even invent your own variations of the story or involve the whole family in some musical dramatic play.

Using the Recording Of course, you will want to have a recording of the song to fully enjoy this book. See page 31 for ways to get the Singalong Storybook songs and see the video "Using Your Singalong Storybook Musically." And if you play an instrument such as piano or guitar, you'll also find it easy to pick out the song using the music page at the end of the book.

Hello, everybody, so glad to see you,

Hello, everybody, I'm so glad to see you!

Hello to Mommy, so glad to see you,

Hello to Daddy, so glad to see you, too!

Hello to Grandpa, so glad to see you,

Hello to Grandma, I'm so glad to see you!

Hello to Mommy, so glad to see you,

Hello to the baby, so glad to see you, too!

Hello I'm Uncle Gerry, so glad to see you,

Hello, I'm Grandma Yvette, I'm so glad to see you!

Hello to my doggie, arf arf arf arf arf,

Arf arf arf arf arf arf
Arf arf arf arf arf arf!

Hello, everybody, we're so glad to see you!

13

Hello to the garden, so glad to see you,

Hello to the carrot, yummy yummy yum yum!

Hello to the houses, so glad to see you,

Hello to the playground, so glad to see you, too!

Hello, I'm a tree, so glad to see you,

Hello, I'm a trolley, ding-a ding-a ding ding!

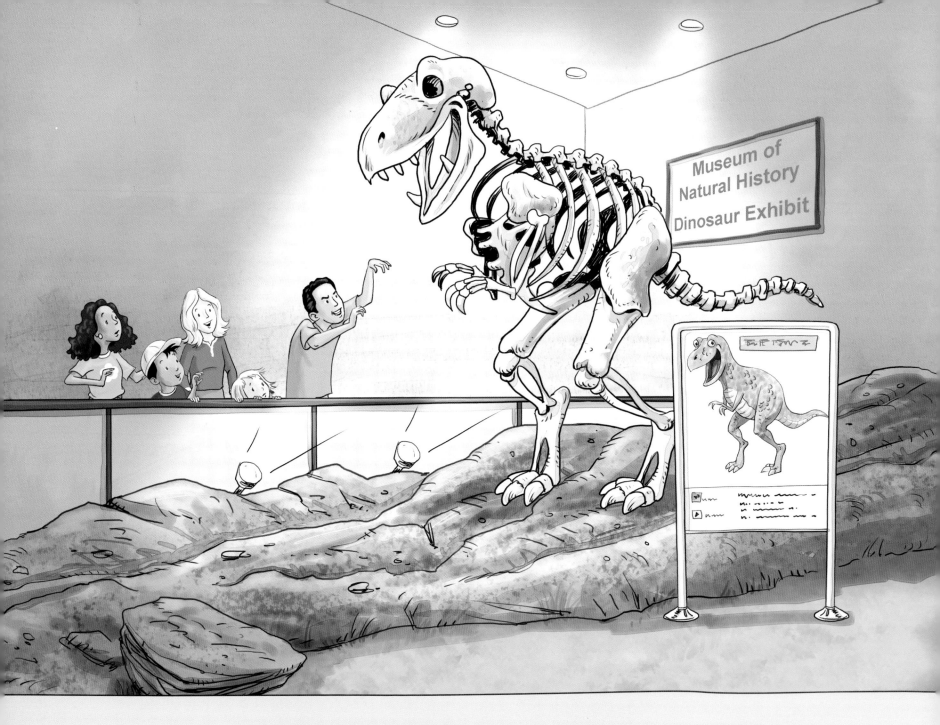

Hello, I'm a dinosaur, roar roar roar roar roar,

Roar roar roar roar roar roar,
Roar roar roar roar roar roar!

Hello, we're the singers, La la la la la,

Hello, we're the band,

Bom bom bom bom bom bom!

Pum brrrum pa-pum pa-pum!   Wah wah wah wah wah wah!

Hello, everybody, so glad to see you,

Hello, everybody, we're so glad to see you!

Activities

"Hello, Everybody!"

The book shows many different ways to sing "hello" to friends and family. A child can sing "hello" to his parents, his grandparents, his stuffed animals, his dog or cat—anyone, anything, anytime!

"Hello, it's me!"

Children like to hear their names and like to sing them, too. Older children may enjoy introducing themselves, especially if the grownups try it first. Each person sings his or her own name—"Hello, I'm Emma"—and the others reply "So glad to see you."

"So glad to see you!"

As a family, you could sing "hello" to everyone sitting at the dinner table or arriving for a birthday party. Sing "hello" to someone coming home from work or from preschool, or just from the other room—and watch the smiles appear!

"Hello" to the world

Children love this song because it invites them to playfully explore the concrete and fascinating world around them. "Hello to my bathtub, so glad to see you! Hello to the bubbles, so glad to see you, too!" What could you sing "hello" to in your house or on a walk down your street?

"Hello, I'm spaghetti!"

Your child may also enjoy pretending to be someone or something else. This could be as silly as "Hello, I'm a rutabaga, so glad to see you," as fierce as "Hello, I'm a monster, grrr grrr grrr grrr grrr," or as heroic as "Hello, I'm Superman, so glad to save you!"

Hello Song

K. Guilmartin

Moderately

| | C | Amin7 | C | Amin7 | F | G7 | C |

Hel - lo_____ ev - 'ry - bo - dy,_____ so glad to see you!

Hel - lo_____ ev - 'ry - bo - dy,_____ I'm so glad to see you!

Hel - lo_____ to *(name)*,_____ so glad to see you!

Hel - lo_____ to *(different name)*, so glad to see you, too!

About the Song

The "Hello Song" is sung at the start of every Music Together class worldwide, to greet each child individually with a warm and inviting welcome. Children happily recognize it as signaling the beginning of music time—and because the tune is so simple and catchy, so fun and easy, it is often the first song they learn to sing. Whenever children and adults think of Music Together, they are likely to find themselves singing, "Hello everybody!"

The words in the book differ slightly from the "Hello Song" lyrics on the Music Together recordings, reflecting some of the variations that our teachers have developed over the years. It's easy to find ways to sing the "Hello Song" all through your day!

About Music Together®

Music Together classes offer a wide range of activities that are designed to be engaging and enjoyable for children from birth through age seven. By presenting a rich tonal and rhythmic mix as well as a variety of musical styles, Music Together provides children with a depth of experience that stimulates and supports their growing music skills and understanding.

Developed by Founder/Director Kenneth K. Guilmartin and his coauthor, Director of Research Lili M. Levinowitz, Ph.D., Music Together is built on the idea that all children are musical, that their parents and caregivers are a vital part of their music learning, and that their natural music abilities will flower and flourish when they are provided with a sufficiently rich learning environment.

And it's fun! Our proven methods not only help children learn to embrace and express their natural musicality—they often help their grateful grownups recapture a love of music, too. In Music Together classes all over the world, children and their families learn that music can happen anywhere, every day, at any time of the day—and they learn they can make it themselves.

Known worldwide for our mixed-age family classes, we have also adapted our curriculum to suit the needs of infants, older children, and children in school settings such as preschools, kindergartens, and early elementary grades. Visit www.musictogether.com to see video clips of Music Together classes; read about the research behind the program; purchase instruments, CDs, and books; and find a class near you. Keep singing!

Getting the Music

The "Hello Song" has been sung in Music Together classes around the world. Listen to the song free at www.musictogether.com/storybooks. The song can also be found on the award-winning Music Together CD **Family Favorites**®. CDs and downloads are available from Music Together, iTunes, and Amazon. To get the most out of your storybook, see the video "Using Your Singalong Storybook Musically" on our website.

The Family Favorites CD includes 19 songs and a 32-page booklet with many family activities to enjoy. Our award-winning **Family Favorites**® **Songbook for Teachers** features techniques and activities to suit a variety of classroom settings.

Come visit us at **www.musictogether.com**.

Music Together LLC

Kenneth K. Guilmartin, Founder/Director

Catherine Judd Hirsch, Director of Publishing and Marketing

Marcel Chouteau, Manager of Production and Distribution

Jill Bronson, Manager of Retail and Market Research

Susan Pujdak Hoffman, Senior Editor

Developed by Q2A/Bill Smith, New York, NY